Orion Books Ltd
Orion House
5 Upper St Martin's Lane
London WC2H 9EA

First published by Orion in 2006

Drawings by Michael Martin

Cover illustrations by Alex Graham

© Associated Newspapers plc 2006

ISBN-13 978 07528 8104 1

ISBN-10 0 7528 8104 3

Printed and bound in Great Britain by
Butler & Tanner Ltd, Frome and London

www.orionbooks.co.uk

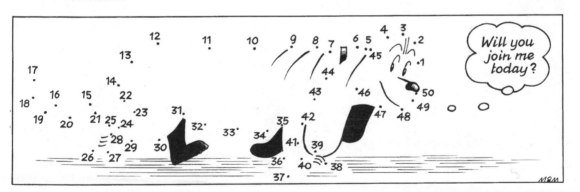

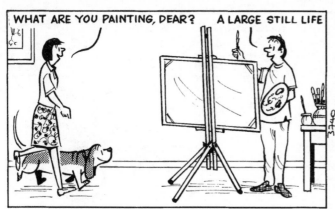

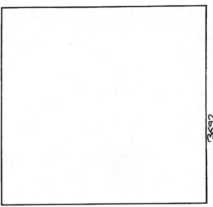